A KISS ON THE NOSE

RHYMES BY TONY BRADMAN
PICTURES BY SUMIKO

PICTURE CORGI BOOKS
A DIVISION OF TRANSWORLD PUBLISHERS LTD.

Also illustrated by Sumiko
My Baby Brother Ned
My School
and published by Picture Corgi Books

A KISS ON THE NOSE
A PICTURE CORGI 0 552 523402

PRINTING HISTORY
First published in 1984 by William Heinemann Ltd.
Picture Corgi edition published 1986
Reprinted 1988
Text copyright © Tony Bradman 1984
Illustrations © Sumiko Davies 1984

Picture Corgi Books are published by:
Transworld Publishers Ltd.,
61-63 Uxbridge Road, Ealing, London W5 5SA.

Printed in Portugal by Printer Portuguesa

For the real authors of the rhymes, Emma and Helen.
Daddy

A new day beginning, out of my bed,
My Daddy will give me a kiss on the head;
Up in the morning and into my clothes,
A kiss on the head and a kiss on the nose.

Into the bathroom
And up to the sink,
This water's for washing,
It's not to drink.

There's soap on my face,
And soap in my eye,
Ooh, wash it all off—
Else I'm going to cry.

This is my toothbrush
And these are my teeth,
Toothpaste tastes nice,
All squidgy and sweet.

I keep brushing and brushing,
And Mummy helps too—
So I've lovely clean teeth,
For smiling at you.

I can put my socks on,
I can find my vest,
I can put my pants on—
I can't do the rest.

This is me.
This is my Mum and Dad.
Do this, they say. Do that.
But today I won't.
I won't get dressed.
I won't brush my teeth.
I won't get in my pushchair.
I won't get out of the pushchair.
I won't tidy up my toys.
And I certainly won't eat my lunch.
I'll scream instead.

I won't play with anyone.
I won't watch the television.
I won't look at any books.
I won't get undressed.
I won't have a bath.
And I certainly won't have my hair washed.
I'll scream instead.
This is me in bed.
I'm fed up. So are my Mum and Dad.
I'm sorry Mum.
I'm sorry Dad.
I won't . . .
be as naughty tomorrow!

Up to the table,
On to my seat,
It's time for breakfast,
It's time to eat.

I start with my cereal,
Then I have toast,
With butter and jam—
That's what I like most.

I drink cold fresh orange,
It wakes up my tongue,
I feel it go sliding down
Into my tum.

Down from the table,
Down from my seat,
My tummy is full up—
And breakfast's complete.

My Mummy had a baby,
And that baby, who was she?

I'll tell you who that baby was—
That baby was ... me!

There was a little tot,
Who sat upon the pot—
Did she do what Mummy asked her?
No she did not!

I've got a tabby cat
Who isn't very nice,
She chases me and bites my toes—
She must think they're mice.

I've got a secret plan,
Just you wait and see,
I'll lock my toes in the cupboard
And throw away the key!

I don't mind the skin
That apples are in,
But I get to the core—
And don't want any more!

Riddley tiddley
My little thumb
Goes bang, bang, bang,
On a big bass drum.

He's the leader
Of a marching band,
Four musicians
On my little hand.

Riddley tiddley,
Toot, toot, toot,
Three big trumpets
And a piping flute.

Four musicians
On my little hand,
With my thumb
Make a marching band!

Take two cushions,
And a chair,
Put them together,
Anywhere.

Add a blanket,
And a rug,
This is my house,
Nice and snug.

Find my teaset,
Fetch it all,
Then I'll ask my friends
to call.

In the morning,
We're so busy,
Mummy says she's
In a tizzy.

Off to playschool,
And the shops,
Mummy says
We never stop.

Then drop in
On Mummy's friends
(Mummy's talking
Never ends).

Back to playschool,
Pick up brother,
We're both tired—
So is mother!

Don't like
My dinner,
Don't want
To eat,
Don't want
My carrots,
Don't like
The meat.

Won't eat
Potatoes,
Won't touch
My cup,
Won't eat
My dinner,
Won't eat
It up!

When I'm feeling tired,
When things go wrong,
When Mummy won't sing
My favourite song,

I'm naughty and nasty,
I'm not nice to know,
I scream and I shout
And a tantrum I throw.

When my stupid brother
Spoils all my games,
When he calls my teddy
Horrible names,

I'm naughty and nasty,
I'm not nice to know,
I scream and I shout
And a tantrum I throw.

But when I say sorry
And I suck my thumb,
I get a nice cuddle
From my favourite Mum!

The little one's thin—
He won't go in.
The next one's shy—
He'll only cry.
This one's strong—
But far too long.
The next is proud—
He'll shout out loud!

And here he sits—
The one who fits!

I load up my trolley,
Pull it along,
I run over teddy,
I sing him a song;

Give him a plaster,
Give him a drink,
Put him to bed now
While I have a think.

Unload my trolley,
Drink from my cup;
Wake up now teddy,
Time to get up!

Up on your shoulders, Daddy,
Up in the air,
Swing me round and round, Daddy,
Tickle me there.

Up on your shoulders, Daddy,
Give me a ride,
Bounce me up and down, Daddy,
Tickle my side!

I'll be the doctor,
You be the nurse,
My dolly's the patient—
She mustn't get worse.

Give her the medicine,
Do it just right,
Now put her to bed
To sleep for the night.

Breakfast, lunch,
Dinner, tea,
Most of my food
Ends up on me.

In my lap
And on my hair
Porridge, orange
Everywhere.

If I eat less,
Or even more—
Most of my food
Ends up on the floor.

Breakfast, lunch,
Dinner, tea,
Food is fun—
At least for me!

This is me.
This is my Mum. And this is my Dad.
This is my nappy.
Sometimes it's wet. Sometimes it's dry.
Sometimes it's full up.
Sometimes it falls down.
I laugh.
Mum doesn't.

This is my potty.
I can sit on it.
I can put it on my head.
I can sit the cat on it.

I can empty it on the carpet.
I laugh.
Dad doesn't.

This is me on the potty.
Sometimes I hear a tinkle.
Sometimes I hear a thud.
Sometimes I go red in the face.
Sometimes I point at what I've done.
I laugh.
So do Mum and Dad.
At last!

Daddy, turn the taps on,
Let the water in,
I'm a fishy in the sea,
A fishy with a great big fin.

Mummy make the bubbles,
When the water's in,
I'll be Father Christmas
With a beard upon my chin

Daddy pull the boats along,
Now the water's in,
I'm the captain on the bridge,
In charge of everything.

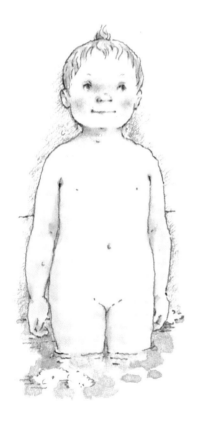

Mummy take me out now,
Leave the water in,
I'll be a slippery porpoise
With a clean and shiny skin.

Fee, fi, fo, fum,
Look out in there—
Here I come!

If you're awake
And not asleep,
Under the bedclothes
I will creep.

If you're awake
And not asleep,
I'll tickle your toes
Till I make you squeak!

Fee, fi, fo, fum,
Look out in there—
Here I come!

A kiss on the nose and a kiss on the head,
Out of my clothes and into my bed;
I'm warm from my hair to the tips of my toes,
Dreaming of morning, a kiss on the nose.

Diggle, duggle,
In my bed,
We've had a cuddle,
Books all read—

Diggle, duggle,
Sleeping tight,
Duggle, snuggle—
Say night night.

Duggle, snuggle,
Suck my thumb,
Another cuddle,
Dreams will come.

Although it's night,
I think I might
Creep out of bed
And poke my head
Round Mummy's door—
Hear Daddy snore!

And if I snuggle,
Diggle, duggle,
I think they may,
I think they might,
Let me stay
With them—all night!